I Wish I Were At Home

A CHILD'S VIEW OF HURTING AND HEALING AT CHILDREN'S HOSPITAL

Potomac Publishing Company
1990

Written by the Patients of Children's National Medical Center

S0-BZQ-233

Children's
National Medical Center

111 Michigan Avenue, N.W.
Washington, D.C. 20010

PRINTED IN THE UNITED STATES OF AMERICA
FIRST EDITION

INTRODUCTION

I Wish I Were At Home is a collection of poems written by some of the young patients at the Children's National Medical Center in Washington, D.C.

These children have suffered very serious injuries and accidents, and, as a doctor, I can assure you that many of these accidents *could have been prevented*. The statistics speak for themselves: nineteen million children a year are injured in preventable accidents; 50,000 are permanently disabled; and 8,000 die from these tragedies.

What is killing the children in this country? Car accidents, drownings, burns, falls, and poisonings. Sadly, most of these tragedies would never have happened if precautions had been taken. I am sorry to say, children like the ones who wrote the poems in *I Wish I Were At Home* were the victims.

I am hoping *I Wish I Were At Home* will bring attention to the serious problem of children's safety in America and help me publicize the SAFE KIDS Campaign—a program of the Children's National Medical Center.

As chairman of the National SAFE KIDS Program, I am working with the staffs of Children's Hospitals all over the country to make sure safety awareness is taught and practiced.

Our goal is twofold: to increase awareness among adults, especially parents, that injuries are the leading health threat to our children today and to educate adults about injury prevention techniques. SAFE KIDS works with national and grassroots coalitions to achieve this goal. We also work with federal, state, and local lawmakers to make childhood injury prevention a public policy priority. These efforts combine toward our ultimate goal—creating a safe environment for our children.

As a pediatric surgeon for over thirty years, I have treated literally thousands of brave children. When I was appointed our nation's Surgeon General, I made it my goal to focus public attention on child abuse and childhood injuries.

That is why I have sent you a copy of *I Wish I Were At Home*. Please read this book and pass it along. By doing so, you will be helping me spread the SAFE KIDS message.

More than that, you will be joining me in my crusade to stop such accidents from happening. The SAFE KIDS Campaign will reach out to all kids and adults by promoting the teaching and practice of safety precautions at home, school, church, and in everyday situations that children encounter in traffic and play.

It is our responsibility as adults to learn the safety measures which will prevent the tragedies that are harming 1 in 4 children in America today.

Only when safety awareness is part of our everyday living will we decrease the numbers of children recovering from injuries and illnesses in hospitals across the nation.

Join me in my crusade to finally turn the odds around in favor of the children. As adults, we owe them a chance at a better life.

January 31, 1990   C. Everett Koop, M.D.

I LOVE MY GRANDMA

My grandmother is as sweet
as a strawberry.
And if stars were sweet,
she would be sweet as them too.
To find out if a star is really sweet,
I would climb up on top
of the tallest tree I could find
and say "star, star, go in my mouth"
and one would come.
I would bite off one of its points
and swallow it.
I think stars must be sweet
because of their shape.
And they are bright as a light.

Herbie, Age 8

THE BALL I RAN INTO THE STREET AFTER

He was supposed to stop but
he didn't, he kept on
going, it wasn't my fault.
That's all I can remember.

The ball I ran into the street after
looks like an apple
dipped in glitter . . .
a rose in a meadow
growing with water and sun . . .
a light bulb for a party,
that I would turn on . . .
a glittering star
next to the moon, flying
on the back of a bird.

I still like my ball
but I wish it were gone so
I wouldn't have gotten hit.

Danielle, Age 9

MY HOSPITAL ROOM

The curtain hangs like
something cool, like the
cool air you feel when you
are standing in the
shade under a tree while the
sun so bright
reflecting the colors
off the sheets. The blue
floor is calm with no
ripples like in the water in a pond.
If there were palm trees, I would
be spending a nice afternoon
at the beach.

Larry, Age 15

TO THE NURSE

I'm sorry
for being so hard on you.
I didn't want to try
to use crutches because
I was tired and wanted
to go to sleep.
I kicked and I cried,
but after a while I
went downstairs and they tried
to put me on crutches.
I just took one step
this time. Tomorrow
I'll try to take two steps,
even though it hurts.
I'm looking forward to playing
basketball and soccer.
My arm will be as powerful
as a kangaroo's tail.
My leg will move as fast
as I ate my chicken yesterday.

Eric, Age 8

BEING SICK IS

Pale blue
like you find in a bruise,
and fuzzy as double vision.
Blobs float
like paint changing puddles,
like clouds of car exhaust.
Sickness goes over your skin
smooth as wet soap.
It goes from your arm
to your stomach
and then to your head
straight as a soldier
on his way to a castle
to deliver a message to the king,
but slow as a piranha.
The world seems very far away.

Meredith, Age 9
Teresa, Age 8

ABOUT IVs

You need a needle, tape
a tube, water medicine—
sometimes a woodblock,
and a good, round vein
to make an "IV".
An "IV" makes you feel better
the way jogging does.
You feel good, but pooped, too,
like a tire
that's rolled and rolled
and lost its air
but gotten where it was going.

Derek, Age 10

AN X-RAY

An x-ray of a baby
is orange and green and shows
the baby has difficulty breathing.
It sounds like music,
bones close to each other.
The baby swallowed a fish
and a bird.
The fish slid down smoothly.
The bird flew down
and landed in the dark stomach.
They fought with each other
and that gave the baby trouble.
They kept fighting anyway.
The baby's breathing
is still like music
only I can hear.
The baby stayed in the hospital
70,000 years and 82 months.
The baby got older.
The fish and the bird stayed young.

Amber, Age 8

TIM'S TRAUMA

I walked in the street,
I walked back out.
Toward the curb
my lights went out.

I woke up on the curb,
an ambulance came,
took me to the hospital,
and my leg was maimed.

I had my surgery,
I got stitches put in.
And I started my day
all over again.

Timothy, Age 13

SOUMYA

The Rice Krispie
is a brown rectangle.
You eat it.
It goes in my tummy
and stays in little pieces.
Rice Krispies live in a blue and
white and red box.
They sit on each other
and sleep in each other's laps
at night, when the moon comes up.

Rice Krispies have one leg
and two eyes
and know how to stand in milk.
They stand and swim
at the same time.

Soumya, Age 4

THE IV

The tubing of the IV
is like a jump rope.
I can't jump rope
because I'm attached to it.
We are best friends.
We go places together
around the hospital.
We are always going to be
best friends.

Chad, Age 8

THE HEART WHO CRIES

The funny heart
throws a brown football
over the fence so high
and down it comes on the tall grass
and makes a little hole in the ground.
I see the heart kick the football
up in the sky past the clouds.
The sky watches.
I'm on a cloud watching too.
I'll catch it and throw it
back down to the city.
The funny heart will cry
because he lost his football.
The sun laughs so hard.

Michael, Age 6

THE MAGIC MIRROR

I am looking at a balloon.
It is like my mirror.
I am admiring myself.
This is the first time
I've seen myself
since the incident.
I see a prince,
the prince of Babylon,
counting his gold.
I see the President
of the United States,
going over important papers.
I see Hulk Hogan,
the ultimate warrior,
building a house.
I see Michael
in a hospital gown,
dozing off.
His right hand is in a bandage.
His fourth finger on his left hand
is also bandaged.
I look like myself,
a handsome little guy.

Michael, Age 10

STEPHEN'S FIRST POEM

Things that are cold:
My room at home
and part of the house.
Ice in the freezer.
Ghostbusters must be cold.
Air conditioning.
Snow lying on the ground.
Santa Claus, because
he comes from outside.
A bird's wing.
My feet without socks.
The color red from a rainbow.
Tires on a car.
Rain falling on your face.
The stars in the sky.
Someone's earring.
The doctor's stethoscope
when it touches your heart.
Bouncing balls and
bad dreams.

Stephen, Age 7

THE ADVENTURE OF THE HICCUPS

They're awfully big
down there.
They hurt when they start.
I have very deep hiccups.
Their color is clear
as a piece of glass.
Their shape is flat
as when an elephant
sits on you.
Let's send them to the man
in the moon.
Let's go to the window
and watch the moon jump.

Carrie, Age 10

POEM OF EVERYTHING

I notice
a little kitten
at the foot
of the bed,
sleeping.

I notice the nurses
visit with
temperature boxes.

I notice the tape
on the telephone,
looking like
a bandaged patient.

I see
a green monkey
hanging on
to my toy's head.

I notice
the scar
on my side
is red.

Tabitha, Age 7

HOW TO MAKE A NIGHTMARE OF A WEREWOLF

In the woods on a spooky dark night
find 5 golden leaves
and chop them into little pieces.
Cut up one worm and make it into 10.
Dip each one into red rainbow sauce.
Add 3 drops of vinegar
and a pinch of unicorn salt.
Find 10 claws from a boy werewolf
on the tops of the trees.
Add a tooth from a stupid human baby
that you steal from the tooth fairy.
Oooooh! Add the oink from a pig
and the howl of an owl. Oooooh!
Mix for 29 minutes using an IV.
Next add ketchup and black pudding.
Cook for 29 minutes in the microwave.
Now we have a nightmare.
Leave it in the forest for Snow White.
When we hear her scream,
we'll know she's found it.

Patrick, Age 7

ABOUT MY GRANDMA

I wish
my grandma
stayed here
for a whole year
and stayed with me
in the hospital
for one day.
And then I want Laurie
to see my grandma
and speak Spanish with her
and talk about me,
about when I'm bad and mean,
like when they give my chemotherapy,
and I tickle the nurses
and that keeps them from doing their jobs.

Rosa, Age 12

POTION TO CURE PAIN

In an IV
put a bit of a pinch
from the doctor's tonsils,
marinated in blood,
a milk carton-full of music,
and a thundercrack of freeze dried potatoes.
Strain through the holes
of the telephone receiver,
and push the buttons 50 times
until you hear the whimpers
of a cat and the cry of a pig.
Boil in the bathtub
for a sweet minute
and stick in a hospital bracelet.
Put in a nightmare of love,
mix with Superman coming to rescue you
with his needle.
With a blink of an eye
he pokes you and the pain turns
into a magical lightdance.

Dawn, Age 16

WISHING

I fell out the window,
the fourth floor open window.
It wasn't like flying.
My brother accidently pushed me
and I fell on my face.
The sidewalk was light white.
The police came and got me
and put me on the steps.
I felt like I was in a dream.
They they put me on the stretcher
and they put me in the ambulance
to the hospital.
Now I am lying down in bed.
I wish I could go home.

David, Age 7

HOW TO MAKE
A HOSPITAL BED

First you take an old nurse.
Chop two small clouds up.
Then you take broken skateboard wheels
and shredded nightmares.
Mix green, yellow, and blue water up
and take an IV pole and a trash can
and a large home.
Take clay and make a snake 8 yards long.
Mix everything up and let it sit
for 3 days. It will look like grey clay.
Roll it all together
and put it in a hospital.
Then chop 9 doctors up,
add blue nail polish, chop up a TV,
and let it sit for 8 more days.
In the hospital.
And then you have your hospital bed.

Lawrence, Age 8

A CAR ACCIDENT

We were coming from my grandmother's house. Then we were going up 6th Street, Northeast, and this car, it ran the light. The Jetta turned over three times. I was in the back seat. I did not have my seat belt on. Mister Chief and my sister had theirs on.

My sister cried "Help." I tried to lift her up but I fell back in the seat. I got up and went out the window. I felt like I was going to die. I hollered for my mother and she came in the ambulance. I was worried about my sister. I felt like people were going to kill me, the way they were tying my legs up. Now I feel like they are going to help me get better.

Migual, Age 6

PRETTY BUTTERFLIES FLYING IN MY STOMACH WHERE THEY DON'T BELONG

My tummy hurts.
It is light inside
and there are red, green,
and purple butterflies.
The red ones are flying real fast.
I can feel their wings
against my stomach.
When someone catches them,
like a little girl,
they will fly away.
The green ones are flying very slow.
They are tired and lazy,
flying below the ground
inside my tummy.
They like when it is nighttime.
Then they get to sleep.
The purple ones keep bouncing
in my tummy.
I wish it would stop.
I'd like them all out and throw them
outside, and let them play
and fly and be lazy.

Nicole, Age 7

RASHEED'S TALES

My cast is as white as the curtain
between me and the next patient.
My cast feels hot as a rock on a stove.
My cast is as rough as a brick.
It's as long as an oversized TV.
I can see my toes.
They are sticking out like five french fries
wiggling in the sky!
They can do tricks:
fly around like lost butterflies
and jump like grasshoppers.

Rasheed, Age 9

THE STUFF THAT WHITE DOES

White,
a pretty color.
A doctor's coat,
the walls of a hospital,
my teeth, all lined up
like corn kernels.
White might smell like water.
It might taste like peppermint.
It makes me feel like
bugging my nurse.

Bobbetta, Age 14

RECIPE FOR A NURSE

Spread out a hospital sheet.
Take a pocketful of good dreams,
add a slice of a red and pink star,
and chopped lullabies.
Blend with a cartoon
and ten fingernails of a cat.
Sprinkle with pink nail polish.
Let stand until Wednesday.
Then pick her up
and put her in the hospital
and let her make you laugh.

Rosa, Age 12

THE WAY I FEEL

When I feel surprised
I am like a bag
full of candy
popping open.

When I feel sleepy
I'm like a boxer
being pushed down
in the ring.

When I feel lonely
I'm like the moon,
out in the sky
with no stars.

When I feel confused
it's like two people
are grabbing my arm
and pulling me
in different directions.

When I feel angry
it's like tons of brussel sprouts
are about to attack me
and I don't want to eat them.

When I feel joy
it's like a bunch
of blue butterflies
filling the air.

When I feel excited
I am like a dog
anxious to go outside and play
with his bone.

Marcus, Age 12

HOW TO MAKE A NEW PLANET

Inside a castle
take one piece of orange clay.
Make the rings of Saturn
by sitting on the clay.
Take a knife and stab the clay
to make holes, then open it.
Then take the game Monopoly
and shred the money.
Chop up a poem and eat it.
Now all the words are inside you.
Take a needle 8 yards long
and stick it all the way into your arm.
Keep it in for a month.
Take the needle out,
with the words on it
like blast-off, hot rocks, and meteoric.
Put a band-aid on your arm
so Martians can't come out.
If they pop out anyway,
leave them alone.
Mix everything up for 4 centuries.
Put it in a round microwave for 9 centuries.
Then shoot it up in the sky with a sling-shot.
Then take a rocket up to the planet
and sprinkle large dust on it—
brown, green, and black, and a little bit
of blue. If it doesn't work
go back to the drawing board!

Binky, Age 8

THE PLUM IS DROPPING OFF THE TREE

When I get a shot
it's like nails
are sticking
into my leg
like a knife.
After a while
it heals.
The needle mark
turns purple
as a plum.

Tikeisha, Age 6

FLUSHED

I'm going to get flushed.
Not down the drain!
This pushes my blood back
into my skin.

When you get a fever
you get flushed.
Your skin turns reddish
and you look like a clown!

Shannon, Age 10

WHEN I CAN'T REACH

When I can't reach
my leg, to itch,
I call the nurse.
Not being able to scratch
is like putting a Christmas tree
in front of me
and not letting me have any presents.
I miss my mother's fingernails!

Tarshieka, Age 9

THE FROG

When you get the hiccups
a little frog inside
bounces up to your chin
and down to your chest
again and again until
you drink some water
and he gets knocked out.

Otis, Age 8

MY BABY BROTHER

As I walk,
the snow falls down,
covering my head, the cars,
the roof of my house.
The snow makes me fall down
because it is slippery as fish.
Rain falls down, and so do babies
'cause they don't know
how to walk yet.
Pine needles from Christmas trees,
water pouring from a faucet,
branches and leaves from trees, rocks
tumbling from hills, hot lava cascading
from volcanoes. The sun and the moon
go down too.
Sometimes my spirit falls down
when I stay in the hospital.
My spirit lifts up when I see
my baby brother.

Rosa, Age 12

RECIPE FOR
A TEDDY BEAR

In a bowl
put one drop of Coca Cola
sprinkled with catsmiles.
Chop up a cloud
with bits of a song.
Mix for three minutes.
Then add a balloon in bloom.
Pour into a pan
and bake for one minute.
Let it cool until you see
a bird fly by.
Remove from pan,
cover with rainbow sauce,
and put onto the television.
Then listen to him sing!

Rosa, Age 12

MY BODY IS AN OCEAN

My ear resembles a half-opened lobster
waiting to be gobbled up
by the treacherous waves.

My mouth resembles a clam
with many rough-edged pearls made of teeth
on a smooth bed of sand
on the bottom of the dark sea.

My dark brown flowing hair
resembles kelp floating
in the crystal clear ocean.

My grumbling stomach
sometimes sounds like the waves
crashing against lovely white sand.

The pitter-patter of little octopuses
on the ocean floor
sounds like a thousand wheels
turning in the night.

Shelley, Age 12

POLES IN THE STREET

My hand has five poles.
They are standing in New York City.
They give people light to drive in.
They are lined up like students
that have been good.
The shortest stands in front
of a grocery store
and is green as a frog.
The tallest puts light on a highway,
and is red as blood.
When I make a fist
they all fall down
and the night is dark and gloomy.

Michael, Age 10

TALKING STARS

Red stars on my nightgown
fly in the air
to meet with more stars.
Stars have mouths.
They talk like people do,
in English, once a month
at a star meet.
If we were stars
we would talk about
keeping our points sharp
and staying shiny and not
getting lost
up in the sky.

Nephetari, Age 5

HOW TO MAKE A CHAIR

Take one broken hospital bed.
Shred it up and put it in an IV.
Add one heart from someone's stomach.
Then take one young nurse,
put her on another bed.
Take an exercise machine
and chopped up moon,
the falling stars,
and music from grass.
One peaceful closet
and Romeo and Juliet.
Mix it all up.
Add sprinkles of light
and a twinkle of cartoons,
three cat whiskers, brown sugar,
and green nail polish.
Mix for 10 days and 10 nights.
Then say the magic words
zoom zee.
Then presto,
and you have your magic chair.

Lawrence, Age 8

Red.
A sad color.
Makes me think of a heart.
A beautiful rose
sitting in a garden.
A fire siren on a truck,
going by my house.
Soft as a white feather.

Purple.
A blushing color.
Grapes in a grapevine.
A velvet dress
with a frilly bottom.
Friday night, when you go out
on a date and you kiss
and you blush.
Shivery as an icicle.

Blue.
The color of dreams.
Clouds as fluffy
as a rabbit's fur.
Blue mountain top
in distant land.
An angry color.
Blueberries cold and juicy.

Sarah, Age 9

THE SUNSET DRIFT

The water is as calm as the sunset.
I am sitting alone dreaming about the future.
Drifting in a boat where ever the water
wants to take me.

The sun looks like a billiard ball.
Its reflection on the water
is like the cue stick
that will send it into the future.

The water takes me to my dream.

Jason, Age 11

THE BRAVE KNIGHT

I'm as brave as a knight.
I fight like a bear.
I stand like stone.
And when I fight
my enemies die at night.

One day the enemies attacked.
The king sent me out
'cause I was leader of the pack.
And when I fought
the swords crashed like light.
All the enemies fell
and we won the war
and only a few of our side fell.

Matthew, Age 9

A little grey fish
usually sits in his tree.
He is the only one there.
We used to have seven,
but a goldfish
ate the five little ones.
Then he died because he ate
too much.
Every time we put a fish in there,
the little grey fish kills it.
Sometimes when I look at him
his eyes are wide open
and looking at something.
Sometimes he looks scared.
Sometimes he just lays in the water
and floats like magic.
If I were a fish
and got put in his tank,
maybe I'd bring him
a television.

David, Age 6

FIVE SENSES POEM

Hate.
Sounds like someone screaming at a person.
Smells like moldy purple hair.
Tastes like hot milk.
Looks like a squished carmobile.
Feels like the top of a pizza, slimy.
Hate makes me feel like jumping
higher than the earth to get away
from my brother.

Santiago, Age 6

MY MOM

My mother is as sweet
as me!
Her eyes are as blue
as my watch.
Her hair has curls
and is black as my hair.
When she laughs
the sun comes out.
She's a great cook.
I wish I were at home.

Otis, Age 8

THINGS THAT
MAKE ME LAUGH

When someone tickles me
under my arms and on my neck,
I feel like I'm a clown.
I sound like I'm crying,
as my laugh explodes into
the air.
I cover myself with a blanket
so nobody will tickle me.
I like it a lot of times, though,
like today, tomorrow,
or the next day.
When I laugh,
my teeth show,
white as a star.

Herbie, Age 8

RECIPE FOR A CAT

The bowl must be pink.
First we put in a pinch
of lightning.
Add a pocketful of red rainbow milk
and dust from a horse's back.
Chop the wings of an airplane
and mix until it shines
like a pot of gold.
Pour into a tray
and sprinkle with rainbow dust.
Bake for two hours at 350 degrees,
and let cool on a chaise lounge
for one hour.
Give it a bath and brush it,
while petting gently.
Then let him go
and look at the neighborhood.
He will know when to come back
when the moon comes out.

Abbey, Age 6

THE MAGIC COLORS

When I open the color pink
fish swim out
all over the universe.

When I open the color red
little leaves come down
with joy.

When I open the color purple
sprinkles come out
and land on the ground
with their best friend, a bird.

When I open the color white
kids slide out
with laughter
and sprinkle the ocean.

When I open the color orange
flowers fly out—tulips
big as wheels!

When I open the color yellow
sprinkles come out at night
and cover the ocean
in a blanket of lilypads
that keeps it warm.

Nicole, Age 7

HOW TO MAKE
FREDDIE COUGAR

In a big black bowl
put a gallon of blood from a human head,
long claws from black cats in the night,
a brown beat-up hat,
the shadow of a knife,
a lady's scream,
the whisper of a man dressed in all black,
the juice from a beetle,
and the slice from a nightmare.
Mix for ten minutes with a spoon.
Put it aside in the basement and lock it.
When you hear him bang on the door,
get in your car and go to a new country.

David, Age 8

THE ROSEBUSH

I see a balloon
that is as purple
as a rosebush.
The rosebush is
round as a beachball.
The rosebush smells
as sweet as grape candy.
If I were a rosebush
coming out of the ground,
I would need rain to grow,
or I'd need someone to water me.
If I saw another rosebush,
I'd play with him.
I would roll a tiny ball to him
and he would roll it back.
We would both win the game!

Keisha, Age 7

HOW TO MAKE
A MIDDLE NAME

First you take your first
and last names and then you
take a nurse called Becky
and sprinkles of crushed names.
Then take one bowl of alphabet soup
and make up your middle name,
what you want your name to be.
Take the alphabets and put 'em
in the microwave for 8 seconds.
The middle-name eater
gets to eat all the cooked letters.
Go to bed that night.
When you wake up at 11 a.m.
go to the middle-name eater,
press the yellow button on his chest.
Stomp your feet 3 times.
Then add chair dust.
Get another nurse named Becky
at Children's Hospital.
Shred her up in the middle-name eater
and your middle name
appears in your brain.

Binky, Age 8

THE BEACH

In summer I like to swim
in the sea that is
blue as a cloud and cold
as winter. The waves
are as large as all the people.
They cover everyone,
and one falls down.
His arms flap in the water
like birds.
One is drowning.
I can help him.
I run into the water
and grab him and take
him away from the beach.
I give him water to drink.

Gabriel, Age 13

A FEELING OF BLUE

Blue,
a bold color.
It helps people when they're in trouble.
A balloon floating in a blue sky.
A shirt my brother is wearing,
stained with Pepsi.
My stuffed bear with an orange tail.
Blue might smell like roses.
My eyes shining at night
when it's dark. Blue
makes me feel as bright
as a light in the sky.

Angie, Age 8

SPLISH SPLASH

My third eye . . .
never uses the bathroom.
never sits in a chair.
can sleep.
can eat an apple.
puts polka dotted clothes on.
can drink milk.
sings a book.
can see a car in a big window.
hears TV.
is as blue as the sky.
can cough, sounding like a heart beating.
can do sign language.

can throw paper in a trashcan like a basketball.
speaks English.
can take a bath,
and say Splish Splash!

Tonya, Age 6

THE TASTE POEM

On the word baseball
I'd put hot chili
to burn my mouth.

On the word reading
I'd put vanilla ice cream
to cool off.

On the word cartoon
I'd sprinkle salt and pepper
to make it tasty.

On the word math
I'd put ketchup to drown it
so I wouldn't taste division.

On the word blue
I'd spread vanilla icing
to make it taste smooth.

On the word nurses
I'd put sugar
to make them taste sweet.

I'll eat this meal
at a crazy restaurant
while the customers stare at me
and then they'd order the same thing!

James, Age 12

MY FAVORITE COLOR

Pink.
My pink watch.
My sneakers and their laces.
Cotton candy at fairs.
Strawberry ice cream.
Bubble gum on someone else's chair.
Nail polish on my mother's ugly hands.
A bedpan lying next to my bed.
A flower blooming in my front yard.
Pink makes me feel happy.

D'Anne, Age 6

THE FROG'S STORY

The basketball
looks like a pumpkin.
When I throw it
into the basket,
it falls down and bounces
under a car or
all the way down
the street.
When it disappears
it might go over the bridge
and into the creek.
A frog sits on it and sings.
He travels to the pumpkin patch,
and picks more pumpkins.
He tapes them together in a line
and rides them all back
to my friend's driveway.
Then the frog will throw them
in the basket
and let them
splat.

John, Age 6

STING HARVEY

I want to put a hat
on stockings
that women wear!
It will be an orange cowboy hat.
I can bend it up and say ho ho ho
to keep it in place.
I put the socks on the puppy!
The puppy will parade up and down
the hallway of the hospital.
I'd have him on a leash,
take him for a walk,
feed him, give him something
to play with, and show him
to all the patients.

Melvin, Age 6

WHAT I SEE IN MY PAINTING

In my design painting
the green is cows,
sheep, and horses,
eating the grass.
Magical snow comes down
light green
on the house where
the animals go.
In the corner
a purple ship
is coming to town
to give the animals
free rides.

Rasheem, Age 5

ABOUT MY TOOTH

When a tooth falls out
most people put it
under a pillow.
But I throw it in the trash.
I don't believe in the tooth fairy
so I just let it be.
If I were a tooth
I'd want to put under a pillow,
on the side for comfort.
If you plant a tooth in the ground,
a tooth tree will grow.
People could pick teeth
and put them under their pillows
and dream of the tooth fairy.

Dia, Age 8

THE SPIRITS

The spirits of a human will come
and go.
And the madness in this world
will always show.
There should be more silence
than there is violence.
The sadness of a boy or girl
will live in a cruel world,
although some of us are safe
from the evil, mad, and hate.
The evilness of this world sometimes lies.
I wish this world would never die.
The spirits of a human will come
and go.
And the madness in this world
I hope won't show.

Anthony, Age 12

WATCHING BASEBALL

One time I went
to watch the baseball
game down the street.
It was dark as a rock cave.
There were lots of lights.
I sat on a little bench next to
a lot of me. They didn't talk
to me, they watched the game,
just like me. It was just
like on TV, they hit the baseball
with the bat. It looked like
an airplane flying fast as a racing
car. When the game was over
I went home and watched
all these monkeys on TV.
Then I fell asleep.

Lateisha, Age 4 1/2

THE BLUE STAR

Blue.
A brave color.
Stars in the sky at night.
The sky in the morning.
Icicle pops that taste like sugar,
with artificial flavoring
that turn my tongue blue.
Blue shoes with sparkles on them.
Sweatshirts with Hulk Hogan
on them. Blue is as cold
as the ocean. I think clowns
cry blue tears. Blue
makes me feel like riding a bike.
Puppet joker hats look like blue moons.

Danielle, Age 9

MAGIC MARBLES

I hold marbles
in my hand.
One could be a golf ball
lying in the grass.
One could be the earth
turning around.
In one, I can see myself,
just the way I am,
a beautiful girl
in the hospital
who wishes she could be
dancing. It feels cold
against my skin.
In another marble
I see a leaf
falling from a tree
through water.

Marquita, Age 8

A VOLCANO ON A CURTAIN

The red circle
looks like a blood cell
enlarged 2,000 times.
It looks like a ring
from a ring toss game.
It looks like a volcano
with a yellow core.
The cold lava is flowing out
forming a river
around the volcano.

Samonté, Age 11

THE FIRE

Above the burned mountain,
fire looks like clouds
rising toward God.
When he looks down
he sees fire, smoke,
and the burned mountain
and the waves on the sea.
He feels sad like me.
I miss the grey color
of the mountains
and the flowers growing there.

Chad, Age 8

THE BIG APPLE CIRCUS

I think unicorns are real,
because I saw one at the circus.
It was white, it had no wings.
Its horn was gold and glittery as
magic rocks. Its skin was silky
and smooth as my mom's scarf.
It ran around in a circle,
then behind a curtain to practice again.
If I were a unicorn I would also be
white. My hooves would be black
as stripes on a zebra.
I would live in the circus
and play with the other unicorn.
We would take turns running around
in the circle. We unicorns dream
about running in squares, hearts,
rectangles, diamonds, and circles.
And we also snore!

Abbey, Age 6

LOOKING OUT THE WINDOW

I see blue water,
with pigeons, parked cars
green and red. The sun
up in the air.
I see a cloud.
It looks like a tiger.
It growls and moves away.
I wave goodbye and look
for another cloud.

Darryl, Age 4

ME

I'm as fast as a roadrunner,
I'm as slow as a turtle.
I'm as big as a whale,
I'm as small as a mouse.
I'm as loud as a lion,
I'm as quiet as a rabbit.
I'm as wild as a tiger,
I'm as tame as a hamster.
I'm as tall as an ostrich,
I'm as short as a fish.
Put it all together
and you've got me.

Ryan, Age 9

WINTER

Once there was a snowflake
that climbed up on a tree
and got one of those red apples.

Another snowflake
could fly like a balloon in the air
and it landed on my tree.

Another snowflake
fell on the tip
of my middle finger.

Other snowflakes came down
on children's heads
and brought them happy dreams.

Chavonne, Age 4 1/2

FEELINGS

When I feel anger
a forest fire
burns beyond control.

When I feel sad
I am like a deep cold lake
that is dark and murky.

When I feel happy
I am like a bright light
that never goes out.

When I feel sleepy
I am like a car
out of fuel
that can't go any further.

When I feel sick
I'm like a snowman
after the weather gets warm,
who just melts away.

Todd, Age 13

SECRETS

I keep my secrets
in the back of my brain.

Secrets are the things I see,
nothing special, just things
I don't want to talk about.

I'm the kind of person
who can be open as a box,
open as a clam and an oyster.
My personality comes out.

Sometimes it feels good
to keep secrets.
They belong to me.

Sometimes it doesn't feel good
but I've promised not to tell.

If I were a secret
I'd live in somebody's brain.
I'd be like a locket
and open to them
if they needed it.

Stacey, Age 10 1/2

THE BUTTERFLY WHO LAY ON THE TREE

A butterfly lies
on the branch of a redwood tree.
He might be thinking about eating,
or waiting for a butterfly friend.
He is freezing in the cold,
so he is wearing a barbie doll jacket
and brown leather boots to keep warm.
He is also waiting for his mom
to bring him apples, fries, and a Coke.
It will be dark by the time
she gets back.
A wolf howls in the distance.
A snake hisses in the bushes.
And the moon shines bright.

Gbemi, Age 7
Sebastian, Age 7

THE BALLOON

Five little balloons
flying in a row.
First one says,
my string's been cut.
Second one says,
Hallelujah!
And the third one says
Bye-Bye!
And the fourth one says
maybe you'll see my cousin
in Washington.
And the last one says
hope you feel better
when you land.

Oliver, Age 9

THE SPINNING MARBLES

When I spin marbles
one looks like it's going dizzy.
One looks sparkely as a unicorn.
One looks like it's dancing,
picking up the light.
It is wearing a pink tutu.
One looks like a hurricane
headed for town.
One looks like a volcano
getting ready to explode.
One looks like a spinning
yellow feather from a baby parakeet.
And one looks like the moon
turning faster and faster
until it stops, until it drops.

Abbey, Age 6

THE WISHING ROSE

I like roses.
They smell like sugar.
They are soft as my skin.
They are beautiful as a rainbow shining.
You can wish upon a rose just like
on a star. I have never done it,
but when I do, I will wish
that I can get better soon and
go home and walk again and have
fun with my friends.
Sometimes we go outside
and play games with balls.
I like to water the flowers
in my garden.
I would like to have a rose
for my own, and make lots of
wishes for myself.

Adriana, Age 10

THE PARTY I WENT TO

I am dancing with people.
The music is gently going
while I'm twirling
and my dress is flowing out.

My dress is white
with a blue belt
and I have pretty wings.
All the people are staring at me
while I do my special dance.

There are people
upstairs on the balcony
and downstairs
the people are crowding around.
My mom and dad
are cheering for me.
I feel so good
I would never want to leave.
But when the party is over
I have to leave.
This is the best party
I've ever been to.

Now it's time to leave.
My dress comes back in
to rest by my side.
I dance the whole way
out the door
into the night,
where the moon is clapping.

Vanessa, Age 7

COMMON THINGS

If I were a bird
you would be the wind
to help me along.

If I were lightning
you would be the ground
I struck.

If I were a baseball
you would be the one
to catch me
and bring me home.

If I were a book
you would be the only one
who would read me.

If I were a pencil
you'd be the one
to sharpen my day.

Sean, Age 11

My dog Chelsea
is as playful as snow
dropping from the sky.
The snow covers the grass,
tress, and houses.
Chelsea lays down in the snow
and makes her own footprints and body.
She doesn't know she makes her body,
she just follows us into the garage.

Sometimes I make my own body
in the snow.
It's like an angel.

Jason, Age 8

THE SKY

I want to write about the sky.
It's blue as the sea, but deeper.
It goes up and far away where the stars are.

When I look at the stars
they look like diamonds
on a black sheet.

I dreamed I was touching a star.
When I woke up
it was shining in my hand.

Abdul, Age 14

THE FLOWERPOT

I got a flowerpot
in my head
like a picture so
I can draw it.
How am I going to
take it out of my head?
With imagination!
No operation needed!

Adriana, Age 10

DINOSAURS

I like their tails, with sharp points.
I am going to color the dinosaur red.
His back is rough with little points.
I wouldn't like to be a dinosaur
because they are too big
and I might be ugly.
I will take one to bed with me tonight.

Anzy, Age 5

RAINBOW

My fingers look like four books
dancing at a party
on the bookshelf in a store.
The little one wishes he were big
like the rest of them.
Everyone keeps laughing at him
because he's small.
Someone might drop him on the ground
and step on him.
He might start bleeding,
someone might break his leg.
A small kid should pick him up
and read him.
He'd find stories about animals
and people inside.
They are mad and crying.
Teddy bears, balloons, people
having a party.
And a rainbow.

Maurice, Age 8

THE MAGIC NIGHT

I am sitting on the top
of a building, nice and warm.
I see the stars
twinkling like shiny metal.
Some of them
make the shape of a rocket,
like I saw on the news.
It is midnight.
I can hear city crickets
talking to me like old friends,
telling me secrets about life.
I promise not to tell anyone.
The clouds look like balloons.
The moon has a face
that looks like me,
handsome and rich.

Kelvin, Age 8

GOING TO THE BALL

I walk in the door
and see all the beautiful people
dancing, their gowns turning
like flowers in the wind.
I walk up the red carpeted stairs.
I feel excited,
in my red gown and golden shoes.
Now I am on the balcony
looking down at the ladies
that are dancing in their lovely gowns.
They are like blossoming flowers.
I walk back down the steps
and a man asks me to dance.
I say yes, I will dance.
We find a spot on the dancing floor
and begin to move
like a tornado.

Elizabeth, Age 8

POEM

I like to play the drum.
Blue music goes bing bing bing
and boom boom BOOM.

Yellow music is a jingle bell
hanging from a Christmas tree.

Red music is a telephone
ringing at my home.
Santa Claus is calling
on my line.
The snowman is on the
wrong line.

When I play blue, yellow and red
music all together
they sound like a poem.

Chavonne, Age 4 1/2

THUNDERSTORMS AND ME

Thunderstorms are hasty
but sometimes you need one
so the flowers and trees
grow as big as you.

We don't need the lightning.
It scares people so bad
they run to their basements
and hide under couches.

I'm like lightning
because I strike things
and I'm real fast.
But we need me!

Thomas, Age 9

THE MARBLE

The marble spins
as fast as the earth.
I can make the marble
stop spinning
and catch it before
it falls to
the ground.
I can't make the earth stop
spinning, but I wish I could.
When I spin, I get dizzy,
and lose my balance
like a bad ballet dancer.

Chad, Age 9

HOW TO MAKE
A RAINBOW

In a gold pan
put in a white feather,
the shadow of a pink horse,
and a pocketful of orange air.
Catch a purple star
flying in the air,
with a butterfly net,
and mix it in the pan.
Add a sprinkle of brown sky
and two drops of water.
Add a slice of red orange
and a gold sprinkle of glitter.
Let it sit for two days.
Take a big stick ten inches long
and put it in the gold pan.
Add a grape circle
dipped in peanut butter.
Cook for 8 minutes in a microwave.
It has to cool for 2 minutes.
Take the stick out of the pan
and put it in your hand.
Use the stick to put the rainbow
over Children's Hospital.

Lorin, Age 6

BUSY

Marbles don't sleep.
They stay up 24 hours
every day
and watch TV
when they get home
from marble school.
They learn how to circle
around a table,
how to hit objects,
and they get spinning lessons.
They never get homework.

Otis, Age 8

SUNSET IN RUSSIA

Over in Russia
the big doors have opened.
A lock has been broken.
The black doors swing
open in a slow silent way.
People with shadows in the sun.
A castle in the background.
There is a shadow
in the distance
looking toward you.
The sun gets redder.
I don't see much left.
The doors have opened.
You may all enter.

Steven, Age 10

SHARING A LIFE

I am a beautiful bunny.
I hop around
like a leaping kangaroo.
I drink dew
from any buttercup I can find.
I'm learning the craft
of Mother Nature.
She is like whistling wind
whisping through my hair.
I make sure all the babies are born.
I have fear of when hunting season comes
because I hear screams
and shouts and be-be guns.
From where I sit
the earth looks like a bouncing ball
that kids throw against a wall.
I know the secret of happiness.
I hold it right in my hand.
It feels like melting sand.
If you want to know,
you hold wet sand and sing.

Katie, Age 9

THE LIGHTNING

The lightning is trying to strike a building
because it thinks the building is angry
at the lightning. The branches
of lightning are strong.
They are growing down.
They are lost on the ground
and turn into seeds
that will become flowers.
One day a little girl
will be riding her bike on the road.
She will stop and smell the flowers.
It won't be raining, but it will be lightning.
She will pick the flowers,
take them to her home,
and bring them to her mom.

Chad, Age 8

BUTTERFLY

The dancers
spinning around
look like white tops
on a table.
Or butterflies
about to land
on daisies.
I would rather be a butterfly
'cause then I could fly
to Disneyworld.
I could cruise through the gates early in the
morning. I'd be the first one in!

Ryan, Age 9

MY SUMMER POEM

I like summer, swimming in pools.
I swim in ten feet of water,
cold as the wind.
I dive off the diving board.
I jump up, do a flip,
and stretch my hands out
like waves.
My hands enter first, and I
disappear under water
and swim under the rope
to the shallow water and push
up high on the surface like a
rushing whale. The sun
drys me off.

Ali, Age 9

I opened up
all the snowflakes
and out popped a world
full of teddy bears.
Inside the world of
teddy bears, out popped
a world full of dolls
like my doll Lollipop.
Her eyes are brown as
a tree stump. Her hair is
in pigtails, with red ribbons.
It's not like she's lost and you
have to find her. She's in
the world of loss where
you can lose anything you
take there. She slid over
the rainbow and finally found
her home with me.

Brandi, Age 7 1/2

HE IS THE QUARTERBACK

He is the key that starts the car.
He is the fuel that makes an airplane fly.
He is the coal that makes the engine run.
When he runs he plants his feet to the grass
like a tree setting into moist ground.
When he throws a ball it's like a bullet
being shot out of a gun that attempts to land
in the receiver's arms as if he were cradling a baby.
When he runs he has the grace of an ostrich.
If he wins he is overwhelmed.
If he loses he mopes back to the locker room
until the following Sunday, when he gets his
next chance.
The herds of people rush for the doors
as the game concludes, like wild Tasmanian devils,
as the stadium sets like the sun going down
behind the Grand Canyon.

Peter, Age 13

MADE OF LITTLE ICY

My ice cream is white
as pillows.
It is cold as ice.
It melts on my tongue
and goes down to my tummy.
It looks like snow.
It smells like you can
make it out of snow.
I like to throw snow
at my friends.
They throw it back at me.
I fall beside the trees
and it gets all over me.

Kianca, Age 6

THE HORIZON

Sitting on a sliding board
going under the white-blue water,
I see bubbles
coming from my mouth.
Inside each bubble
is a rainbow.
When the bubbles pop
I see every color
turn into a fish.
When my head pops,
it pops out of the water,
and I see blue, orange, green,
red, white, purple, and black
fish, swimming toward
the horizon.

Patrick, Age 7

MY UNCLE'S GARDEN

In my uncle's garden
there are large blueberries,
as blue as I am when I'm cold.
They get eaten first.
The small ones hide
behind dark green leaves.
They are afraid
of my uncle's rough hands.
The potatoes have eyes
that are looking suspiciously
at the carrots, because they grow
down, while other vegetables
grow up. Their hairs reach out
like arms in the dirt
for water and minerals.
If I could reach out
into my uncle's garden,
I'd pick the sweet corn
and feel it melting
in my mouth.

Erin, Age 10

SUGARPLUM

My mom
is as sweet as sugarplums.
When I bite into a sugarplum,
little sparkles of juice
squirt out on my brother's face.
I can't bite my mom,
but I know what's inside her
is love, affection, coffee and tea,
and the wind that blows
her kisses around.

Ebony, Age 8 1/2

THE TULIP FLOWER

I am happy to be in the grass
watching people walking and talking.
I like the spring the best
because there are more flowers and animals.
I am a yellow tulip
with smooth skin
and green leaves with lines.
Other tulips are my friends.
Only people have power
to cut us out of our grass.
But we tulips have power
to stand up, to grow up,
and come back year after year.

Elisa, Age 8

NATURE

The ceiling could be
the crack of dawn.
The sun is climbing
its way up.
Behind the dark cloud
the day fully opens.
Birds are chirping,
pigeons are flying.
The cloud leads the sun
back to its cupboard,
to the depth of the earth,
the crack of dusk.

Michael, Age 10

THE FEELING OF AIR

We can't see the air
but we can feel it blow past
as we walk through the forest.
It makes the trees sway
as if they were tilting toward
the ground, looking for beautiful leaves
in a puddle
to take them up
onto their branches
to dry.

Washica, Age 10

AARON'S POEM

Lying in bed
I think about remote control cars,
bravery stars,
and my balloon that's losing air
that soon will be small
as an egg.

Aaron, Age 7

THE LIFEGUARD STORY

Swimming in a pool
is like being in grape soda.
You can make bubbles.
If you close your eyes
and go way out,
you can get lost.
The water magicians rescue you
and put you back on land.
This never happened to me.

Migual, Age 6

MY HANDS

My fingers look like trees
with no leaves.
They drop to the ground
like slippers in the wind.

My fingers look like a happy peacock.
The four big feathers
make him look pretty
by spreading their colorful feathers out
with a flipper sound
that birds make when they fly off.
When the feathers move,
sometimes a fly comes by
and they tickle it.

There is road on my palm
that turns off to my second finger.
At the end there is a haunted school
that crickets hop in
and scare people
because of their squeaky noise.

My fist looks like
the four ballerinas bowed
and the white curtain closed
and when the audience clapped
it made a slapping noise
with both of your hands.

Katie, Age 11

AT THE PARTY

At the party
I drank soda,
warm and fizzy.
And it got in my eyes.
It jumped up!
I ate soft cake.
We sang Happy Birthday
to Nicole,
who is my friend.
I gave her a kiss
on the cheek.
I gave her a hung.
I gave her a smile.

Kimmy, Age 4¹/₂

BUBBLE GUM

I chew bubble gum
while I'm lying down.
I make a bubble and
it pops over my mouth.
The gum is blue.
I'm going to chew on it
for the whole week!

Kimmy, Age 4 1/2

HOW I DO THINGS

When I am swimming
my hands feel like I am cutting
through paper like a pair of scissors.
The paper is sky-blue,
smooth as a wet path,
with a secret code
that says splish splash
only to me and the fish,
talking beneath the surface.

Angie, Age 8

JOBS

A tooth's job
is to come out.
You put it under your pillow
and the fairy comes and
sends a dollar.

A crayon's job
is to color
zebras black and white
and monkeys brown.

A heart's job
is to get cut out.
You pick it up
and then hang it up.

A Kleenex's job
is to blow in
and wipe your nose.

A sock's job
is to warm your feet up
and then get washed.

Ashley, Age 4¹/₂

MY SOUL

When I'm asleep
my soul leaves me
and sneaks into my dreams.
She tip-toes on her toes
like the ballerina
I want to be
at the beginning of the show.
She wears pajamas, sleeveless,
with ruffles where the arms come
and make a moon around her face.
Lavender buds
bloom across the room
she is writing cursive "e's"
only it's with her legs.
She comes back to me
when she gets tired.
That's when she's ready
to call my body home.

Katy, Age 7

WAR BATTLES

The world is like a body
covered with sores.
When a bomb explodes,
blood comes out.
Tanks go right through
and break the whole self.
It can kill you,
that's for sure.
Thousands of bullets
make a big battle
like thousands of needles
when right through
and all the blood comes out.
If there's no help—
no towels like they brought me—
if the world looses too much blood—
it'll get smaller
and then die.

Renaud, Age 7

THE COLOR OF THE HEART

The heart shape
is a sign for love.
I like hearts to be
certain colors.

Red hearts make me feel like
I'm sitting on the top of the world,
looking down at people
small as little dots walkin' around.

Purple hearts make me feel like
I'm floating around in space
bumping into stars one by one,
passing satellites.

Pink hearts make me feel like
I'm on a roller coaster
with my heart dropping
down to my feet.

Blue hearts make me feel like
I'm sailing in a raft
on the ocean, with nothing
but big waves and tiny waves
in the distance.

Shannon, Age 10

On the day of November 17, 1981, Dr. C. Everett Koop was sworn in as the United States Surgeon General. His appointment capped a distinguished career in pediatric surgery.

Born in Brooklyn, New York in 1916, he enrolled in Dartmouth College and he received a B.A. in 1937. Later, he received an M.D. degree from Cornell Medical College and began an internship at Pennsylvania Hospital.

His academic accomplishments were considerable. He did his graduate training at the University of Pennsylvania School of Medicine, Boston Children's Hospital, and the Graduate School of Medicine, University of Pennsylvania from which he received the degree of Doctor of Science (Medicine) in 1947. He was appointed Surgeon-in-Chief of Children's Hospital of Philadelphia in 1948 and served in that capacity until 1981.

Dr. Koop was the sixth pediatric surgeon to practice in the U.S. and the first to practice on children exclusively. During his years of distinguished service, he is credited with having made anesthesia safe for children, and subsequently, he went on to innovate new pediatric surgical techniques. He also developed the first neonatal ICU, pioneered extensive cancer treatments for children, and perfected ways to correct birth defects.

He has written about the practice of medicine, biomedical ethics, and health policy in over two hundred articles and books. Several groups and countries have honored him for his tireless good works, including the government of France who awarded him the Legion of Honor.

During his eight years as Surgeon General, Dr. Koop helped educate this nation about some of its most frightening diseases and social ills.

In 1989 he retired from the office of Surgeon General and decided to make children his personal crusade by campaigning for stricter safety standards and parental caution.

Dr. Koop is now the Chairman of the National SAFE KIDS Campaign, a project of the Children's National Medical Center in Washington, D.C.

Safe Kids Are No Accident

As part of Children's outreach activities, a five-year National **SAFE KIDS** Campaign was established in 1987 to increase awareness about accident prevention. Spearheaded by the Emergency Trauma Services Department and presently chaired by former U.S. Surgeon General C. Everett Koop, the Campaign is a program of Children's National Medical Center and is supported by Johnson & Johnson and the National Safety Council. For free information on the National **SAFE KIDS** Campaign please write:

SAFE KIDS
Children's National Medical Center
111 Michigan Ave., NW
Washington, DC 20010-2970